Jo Thomas has lived in Dorset since 1940, and was educated in Poole with a strong historical bias. In 1972 the Open University provided the opportunity to discover the wonders of science, and the study of geology put history into perspective. After several years recording sites of geological interest for the Dorset Environmental Records Centre, her study of the quarries has continued with the history of their exploitation for building materials. She is now the secretary of Dorset's Important Geological Sites, a group dedicated to encouraging public understanding of the geology of Dorset.

Following page
Cottages in Corfe Castle. Virtually the entire village is built out of cut pieces of Purbeck limestone. Slabs from thinner beds are used as roofing tiles.

DISCOVER DORSET

STONE QUARRYING

JO THOMAS

THE DOVECOTE PRESS

Part of the tower of Knowlton church, showing flint,
Greensand, Chalk and a dark heathstone
known as Lytchett Matravers Sandstone.

First published in 1998 by The Dovecote Press Ltd
Stanbridge, Wimborne, Dorset BH21 4JD

ISBN 1 874336 61 X

© Jo Thomas 1998

Jo Thomas has asserted her rights under the Copyright, Designs
and Patents Act 1988 to be identified as author of this work

Series designed by Humphrey Stone

Typeset in Sabon by The Typesetting Bureau
Wimborne, Dorset
Printed and bound by Baskerville Press, Salisbury, Wiltshire

A CIP catalogue record for this book is available
from the British Library

3 5 7 9 8 6 4 2

CONTENTS

INTRODUCTION

The infinite variety of Dorset's geology is reflected not only in the landscape but also in its buildings. Before the end of the nineteenth century most were constructed of whatever material was closest to hand. Stone quarrying in Dorset has been an important industry since medieval days, particularly in the Isles of Portland and Purbeck, but these still nationally famous industries are simply the most visible remains of a previously widespread activity. There were once thousands of small quarries, forgotten for at least a generation, which for centuries provided building stone, roadstone, lime and sand for their local area. The amount of quarrying activity has been dependent on changing demands: periods of population expansion have required more building stone, with sand and lime for mortar; shifts in farming practice have required lime to spread on the fields.

The Romans, Saxons and Normans all quarried stone for religious and domestic buildings and many more churches were built in the Middle Ages. Most were of local stone, but Purbeck limestone was carried at least as far as north east Dorset for building, and all over England for fonts and carved shrines. The Dissolution of the Monasteries in the sixteenth century meant that the great Abbeys were demolished and their stone used for other buildings, and the new landowners started to build themselves grand houses. Agriculture was prosperous in the seventeenth century with sheep on the Chalk uplands, dairy on the valley pastures and flax and hemp on clay soils, particularly in West Dorset. Improvements in agriculture during the eighteenth century often led to consolidation of farms and larger holdings, which also encouraged the larger landowners to

A general view of St Aldhelm's Quarry. The quarry is the only working quarry in Purbeck providing Portland building stone and is important as the sole source of Spangle, whose calcite crystals sparkle in the light.

build bigger houses. The Newfoundland trade, sending ships from Poole and Weymouth to catch cod, which was traded for sugar in the West Indies, or salt in the Mediterranean, required flax and hemp for sails and ropes. The industry based on Bridport resulted in more building by prosperous mill owners. The Napoleonic wars in the late eighteenth and early nineteenth century brought more prosperity particularly to West Dorset because ropes and sails were needed for the navy. However, depression after the wars meant that little building was done until after 1850. In the latter half of the nineteenth century the population began to expand, largely due to improved healthcare and housing provided by philanthropic industrialists. Workers' houses were built of stone in the towns which must have contrasted strongly with the cob hovels of the agricultural workers.

Each century has provided a market for building stone, but apart from on the Isles of Portland and Purbeck, quarrying activity has been on a small scale, often carried out by farm labourers when the weather was unsuitable for agricultural work. Churches, houses and farm buildings have been repaired or wholly rebuilt many times as stone weathered away, fashions changed, or populations expanded. The tenants of a parish were given the right to draw stone whenever they required it for repairs. The best quality stone has survived the weather, and the masons' style of work often gives a clue to the age of parts of a building, which in turn can suggest when the quarries were being worked. A medieval wall looks totally different from a Victorian one, but the Victorian quarry can be seen on a map whereas a medieval one would be hard to find.

The geological map of Dorset shows that the county can be divided into areas; divisions dependent on the rock type present. Although all the rocks are sedimentary and result from the deposition of sand, mud or limestone in water, the conditions under which they formed are very variable. In addition to the movement of continents, climates and sea levels have changed many times over millions of years. During the Jurassic (146-208 million years ago) and Cretaceous (65-146 million years ago) periods what is now the European continent was closer to the equator than today. The water was considerably warmer and extended over the continental

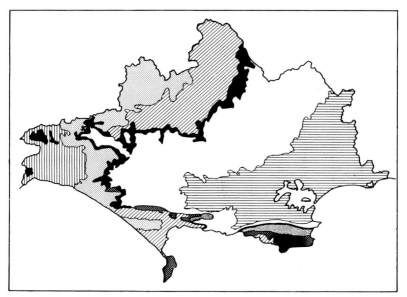

A simplified map of the geology of Dorset.

Tertiary rocks (clays, sands & gravels).

Chalk (limestone).

Lower Greensand, Gault & Upper Greensand (clays & sands).

Wealden (clays, silts, sands & grits).

Portland Sand & Stone & Purbeck Limestone Group (limestones & clays).

Kellaways Beds, Oxford Clay, Corallian & Kimmeridge Clay (limestones & clays).

Inferior Oolite, Fuller's Earth, Frome Clay, Forest Marble & Cornbrash (limestone & clays).

Lower, Middle & Upper Lias (thin limestones, clays, silts & sands).

margins, where limestone was deposited originally as a lime mud on the sea floor. The later Tertiary (1.6 – 65 million years ago) rocks formed on land, or in shallow seawater as the continent was moving northwards. No limestones were formed in Dorset at this time, therefore the eastern heathlands have little building stone of their own.

The majority of quarries in Dorset were opened for building limestone, and although few have been working since the beginning of the Second World War, it is still possible to see the remains of the larger ones. Most of the limestones were formed in the Jurassic period. The individual limestone beds of Jurassic rocks are usually less than 1 metre thick. The thickest beds, such as those from the Portland Limestone, are cut as ashlar, while the thinner beds may be broken, or dressed to shape by hand. Some of them are rich in the fossil remains of ammonites, belemnites, bivalves, gastropods, brachiopods and occasionally plants. The larger fossils may create weak points in a rock which make it unsuitable for building purposes, whilst an even-textured limestone will withstand weathering. The best quality often has crystalline or 'sparry' calcite, cementing grains of lime mud or small pieces of shell together. The best quality freestone, oolitic limestone, is made up of balls of hard calcite and can be cut and used in the same direction in which it lay in the ground, or placed vertically. The ooliths form on the sea bed when a small piece of shell or a sand grain is rolled around by the currents or waves. If the physical conditions are suitable the calcite dissolved in sea water will precipitate out, and the grain will become coated with a fine shell, like an egg shell.

Limestones are defined as consisting essentially of calcium carbonate and are divided into three major groups, organic, chemical, or detrital. Organic limestones consist mostly of the remains of plants and animals which had shells or skeletons of calcium carbonate. Chalk is the purest example, consisting almost entirely of the calcareous skeletons of coccoliths (a floating alga). Other organic limestones are largely made up of shells, corals, or calcareous plankton. Chemically precipitated limestones can be formed by the precipitation of calcium carbonate from warm shallow water caused by evaporation, or by coating sand grains, algae or small scraps of shell with calcium carbonate 'shells' to form ooliths. Detrital limestones are made up of fragments of pre-existing limestone, or organic carbonate. The fragments are cemented together, either with micrite, a powdery calcite, or sparite, a coarse crystalline calcite.

In the Table on the opposite page, the name of the building stone is given in the left hand column, and the geological formation in which it is found in the right hand column. The ages are only approximate, as there is no way of dating sedimentary rocks, except by relating them to igneous rocks containing minerals which change

BUILDING STONES QUARRIED IN DORSET

BUILDING STONE	GEOLOGICAL FORMATION

Quaternary (from the present to 1.5 million years ago)

Flint, often yellow/orange stained	Terrace gravels
Chert	Drift (from Chert Beds of Upper Greensand)
Flint, often red stained	Clay with flints

Tertiary (1.6-65 million years ago)

Hengistbury ironstone	Barton Beds
Heathstone	Poole Formation
Lytchett Matravers Sandstone	near base of London Clay

Cretaceous (65-146 million years ago)

Flint	Upper Chalk
Chalk Block	Lower, Middle or Upper Chalk
Eggardon Grit	Upper Greensand, in West Dorset
Chert	Upper Greensand, in West Dorset
Shaftesbury Sandstone	Upper Greensand, in North Dorset
Coarse Quartz Grit	Wealden
Purbeck Marble	Upper Purbeck
'Burr' (Broken Shell Limestone	Upper Purbeck
Laning Vein, Freestone Vein, Downs Vein and New Vein	Middle Purbeck

Jurassic (146-208 million years ago)

Cap, Slatt and Cypris Freestones	Lower Purbeck
'Portesham' Stone, or White Freestone	Portland Limestone (on Ridgeway)
Roach, Whit Bed and Base Bed	Portland Limestone (on Isle of Portland)
Blue Bed, Spangle, Pond Freestone and Under Freestone	Portland Limestone (on Isle of Purbeck)
Osmington Oolite, Todber Freestone, Abbotsbury Oolite and Cucklington Oolite	Corallian Group
Cornbrash	Cornbrash, Lower
Forest Marble, shelly limestone and siltstone	Forest Marble Formation
Fullers Earth Rock	Fullers Earth, Great Oolite Group
Inferior Oolite, including Sherborne Building Stone	Inferior Oolite
Junction Bed	Middle/Upper Lias
Thorncombe Sands Doggers	Middle Lias
Blue Lias	Lower Lias

over time. Some minerals, like uranium, decay in a known period of time to a different form. Therefore the rocks containing them can be dated within a few million years. The sedimentary rocks above or below these igneous rocks can then be given a relative date. Since sedimentary rocks contain fossils such as ammonites which evolve into different shapes fairly rapidly, the same fossils in different rocks can be used as an approximate time scale.

QUARRYING METHODS

In an area of sedimentary rocks such as Dorset, the harder limestones or sandstones form prominent features of the landscape, protecting the hilltops or forming ridges on the slopes. The first and easiest form of quarrying was therefore to lever out large boulders to use for building. Trial and error sorted good stone from poor over centuries, and an outcrop could be followed over the top of a hill, or round its edge. Open excavation was possible where the stone formed the capping of a hill. A stone which had proved its worth would be followed into the hill, removing the unwanted rock and soil (over-burden) to spoil heaps behind the working face. These spoil heaps are a feature of the large Portland quarries, but the smaller ones have left more subtle clues. Sloes Hill, west of Bridport, can be seen from the rest area on the by-pass. The uneven top of the hill consists of spoil heaps from the Inferior Oolite limestone quarry. From Corfe Common look south to Kingston – half way up the hill are the spoil heaps of old quarries in Purbeck limestone. On the hillside south of the Priests' Way are the spoil heaps from the mines dug into the hill by the early quarrymen. In the open hillside quarries when the overburden became too deep quarrying would stop, leaving a sheer cliff, as can be seen in the car park above Kimmeridge, or on the side of Chalbury Camp near Preston, Weymouth.

In thick freestone beds it was possible to continue underground forming caverns which can still be seen in the cliff quarries in the Isle of Purbeck. The roof of a cavern would need to be supported, either by leaving stone in situ or by building supports before moving for-ward. Only thick beds of rock with few joints could be mined in this way. The cliff quarries of Purbeck are beginning to collapse only 60

Quarrying on Portland in 1932. The stone was cut out by hand, and cranes used to bring it up from the deep pits.

years after being abandoned, whereas in the more solid Chalk of Beer in Devon the Norman quarry-caverns are still open. Thinner beds of stone could be followed into the hill by cutting passages, or adits, the remaining stone holding the passage open. In Purbeck the adits were known as lanes and many have now provided a home for bats. Before large earth-moving equipment became available in the 1950's, mining into a hill was a common practice.

To remove a block of stone from its bed the quarrymen took advantage of the bedding planes (horizontal divisions) and joints (vertical breaks). Any soft clay on the planes was picked out with a pick-axe. Then a bar was pushed under the stone and sheer muscle-power used to lever it out. At Gannets Quarry near Todber the quarryman remembers that an 8 foot bar could be used to lift 10 tons of stone – provided there were enough men to lean on the bar! Once the block of stone had been quarried it could be split using "plug and

Quarrymen on Portland using 'plug' and 'feathers' to split a large block of Portland limestone in the 1930s.

A rare photograph of a North Dorset quarry in Corallian limestone. It shows Gannets Quarry, Todber, in the 1920s. The stone was removed by hand, using the long bar and pickaxe shown amongst the tools on the right.

feathers". This involved chiselling a line of wedge-shaped holes into which a wedge (the plug) with two strips of metal (the feathers) either side was hammered until the stone split. Frame saws were invented in the seventeenth century, and succeeding forms of power have driven saws with increasing speed until today both reciprocating and circular saws have diamond tipped or tungsten teeth.

A water-cooled circular saw cutting a block of Portland stone.

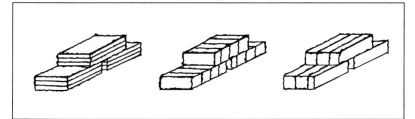

Stone is normally used in its natural bed (left), but for cornices, cills and arches it is placed on edge (centre). Thickly bedded freestones can be face-bedded (right) but others are vulnerable to frost.

MASONRY

Architects refer to masonry as either ashlar or rubble. Ashlar is cut square from thick smooth stone such as Portland, the best Corallian Freestone, or Shaftesbury Sandstone, and built with the minimum of mortar. Rubble refers to all other stonework, but most is dressed stone which has been first roughly broken with a long handled hammer and chisel, or a guillotine, then dressed to shape by hand with a hammer and bolster or an adze. Masons usually lay stone in the same orientation as it was in its natural bed, but occasionally it is used 'out of bed' with the horizontal beds of stone placed vertically.

Cornices and cills are traditionally edge bedded. Similarly, arches are edge bedded in order to transfer the load correctly. Face bedding may be successful with certain freestones such as those in Portland, and the Freestone bed in Purbeck, but in other cases results in frost and rain attacking the fabric of the stone so that it flakes away. An example of this may be seen in Sturminster Newton, where a nineteenth century schoolhouse in Church Lane has a wall facing the road built of Ham Hill stone placed vertically, and where layers of shelly limestone are falling away.

THE WESSEX VALES

A wide sweep of west and north Dorset is underlain by a rapidly changing succession of Jurassic limestones, sands and clays, reflecting changing sea levels during Jurassic times (208-146 million years ago). All the different limestones have been used for building, roadstone or lime, several of the sands for mortar, and the clays for bricks. The later movement of continents caused the beds to break up and tilt and early in the Cretaceous period (146 million years ago) these tilted rocks were pushed up to become dry land, finally weathering down to a flat plain. When sea level rose again several million years later marine sediments were deposited which formed the Upper Greensand and Chalk. Further continental movement has brought the area above sea level again, and in more recent times most of the Upper Greensand and Chalk has been eroded away in West Dorset, leaving the Jurassic rocks exposed.

In the western area the limestones form small hills, as the underlying rocks have been cut by many small faults allowing weathering to erode the softer sands and clays into steep valleys. Around the Marshwood Vale the larger flat-topped hills have been formed by the Cretaceous Upper Greensand Chert beds, often capped by the chert drift which was formed by freeze-thaw weathering during the Ice Ages. In the northern area the limestones form ridges across the countryside, as all the rocks are dipping south east. The sands and clays have been eroded into long sinuous valleys.

The large scale quarries on the Isles of Portland and Purbeck are also in Jurassic limestones, the quarrying methods reflecting the changes in technology which have taken place over hundreds of years. Although of smaller area, the quarries on the Ridgeway between Dorchester and Weymouth are in the same age rocks.

Folding and faulting has been so intense in the Isle of Purbeck that on the Chalk ridge the beds of Chalk on the southern side of the ridge are almost vertical, with horizontal beds on the northern side of the Purbeck Fault. The sands and clays of the Wealden Beds in Swanage Bay dip to the north underneath the Chalk. The uppermost Purbeck Beds have been squeezed into tight folds at Peveril Point where the Marble Beds form the reefs, but most of the inland quarries are worked from comparatively flat-lying beds of limestone.

The Isle of Portland shows gently southward dipping beds which are also the result of folding. The Jurassic beds around Weymouth have been arched upwards into a dome (an anticline). In the process many cracks (faults) appeared and blocks of land were pushed up or down, breaking the continuity of the beds. The processes of weathering and erosion in the millions of years since have worn away the softer clays to the north of Portland, leaving the hard Portland Limestone to form the island.

CENTRAL CHALK DOWNLAND

Over central Dorset the Chalk downlands remain, and the surface rocks are roughly horizontal. On the fringes of the downs deep coombes have been carved through the Chalk to the Greensand below by freeze-thaw action during the Ice Ages. Although Dorset was not covered by ice at any time, the climate was so cold that the surface was frozen during the winter. Spring thaws of snow and water in the soil created considerable run-off forming deep coombes, as streams ran into the river valleys. On the coast, where marine erosion has cut back the cliffs, the gravel deposited by these streams in their lower reaches can now be seen filling the old stream channels

Wimborne Minster, much of whose attraction stems from the
heathstones with which it is built.

in hanging valleys, There are hundreds of Chalk pits, most of which
have been used for the manufacture of lime, and a few quarries in the
sandstone of the Upper Greensand Formation which have produced
building stone.

THE DORSET HEATHS

The heathlands of East Dorset and around Poole Harbour have
developed on Tertiary sands and clays which produce very acid soils,
as they contain no lime. Faulting and folding has affected the eastern
part of the county in at least two periods of continental movement,
so that a basin was formed during the early Tertiary period (about 64
to 36 million years ago). In this basin sands and clays were deposited
on top of the Chalk by a river and estuarine system. The exposed
Chalk was being weathered, and sea-level fluctuated considerably.
Deposition of sands and clays was not continuous in Dorset during
the Tertiary period, but several different clays have been extensively
dug in the past for brick-making and pottery, and sands used more
recently for the manufacture of cement. Quarrying for building stone
has been rare as there is little hard sandstone which is suitable.

[18]

WESSEX VALES

LYME REGIS AND MARSHWOOD VALE

The oldest Jurassic rocks of the Lower and Middle Lias (about 200 million years old) can be seen in the cliffs from the county border west of Lyme Regis to Eype Mouth near Bridport, and occupy the low ground inland. On the high ground, forming a rough circle round the Vale, outliers of Cretaceous Upper Greensand (140 million years old) cap the large, flat-topped hills. Between the two there is a gap in time, but not in space, so that rocks of different ages form the hills, and are used together as building stones.

BLUE LIAS The clays and limestones of the Lower Lias beds were deposited in marine conditions. The Blue Lias is a series of alternating shales and limestones, the shales being paper-thin and easily weathered away by rain and sea. Quarrymen gave the limestones names such as Table Ledge, Fish Bed, Grey Ledge, Glass Bottle, Top Quick and Venty. The limestones are all fine grained and a blue-grey colour, containing bivalve, ammonite and vertebrate fossils. When used for building, as in Lyme Regis, they have proved rather soft and need to be covered with tiles, or rendered to keep out the rain. Until the recent sea wall was built the arch of the fourteenth century Buddle Bridge was pounded by gravel thrown up by the sea, and often needed repair. Some stone has been quarried from the cliffs, also from the ledges, leading to a disastrous effect on the town's stability. Much of the Blue Lias used in the town was quarried at Uplyme where the lower beds of stone used for burning into lime were usually undermined, the upper beds falling under their own weight rather than being cut out. That this was a dangerous practice is shown by a newspaper report of 1865 when George Huxford, Eli Cox and a boy of 16 named Gosling were buried by a fall. In March 1868 several boats were launched again to continue stone works on the western cliff at Lyme Regis and later in the same month an extensive landslip buried a few tons of the limestone excavated by the stone-boat men.

During the eighteenth century the limestones were used for stucco or interior plasterwork, and nineteenth century building specifications refer to Lyme Regis lime for mortar. Blue Lias has been used throughout West Dorset for paving, either inside houses or in the streets, but much of this may have come from Somerset. It has also been used for kerbstones, as can still be seen in Sherborne and Shaftesbury, though it is gradually being replaced by harder wearing igneous rock, or cement which is cheaper. Cobbles from the beach have been used for rough walling in the villages near the coast, such as Charmouth and Wootton Fitzpaine. The cement factory at Charmouth was built in the 1850s, but was only working for about 10 years. Small weathered pieces of limestone, known as cobbles, were collected from the beach in baskets by women working in pairs, but the amount of limestone weathering out of the cliffs was too small to keep the factory working for long.

From Golden Cap to Eype Mouth the cliffs are composed of a series of clays and very fine sands (Middle Lias). None of the sands are suitable for building, but the clays have been used for brickmaking in the valley inland of Golden Cap. The clay was dug from the field and the bricks fired in a small kiln.

UPPER GREENSAND CHERT In western Dorset only the Chert from the Upper Greensand has been commonly used for buildings. At Lyme Regis the lowest grey sands of the Upper Greensand contain doggers (rounded boulders) called Cowstones (they look like recumbent cattle) which were gathered from the beach and used to build the Cobb, first constructed in the reign of Edward I. Forde Abbey, being so close to Chard, has been built of white coarse-grained sandstone (Eggardon Grit) quarried from above the Chert Beds at Chardstock, mixed in the walls with the Chert. The barns at Lower Kingcombe and Toller Fratrum contain many blocks of the Grit in addition to flint from the Chalk.

The Marshwood Vale, according to a local inhabitant, is a place of sodden clay, undrinkable water, and few dwellings. The villages cling

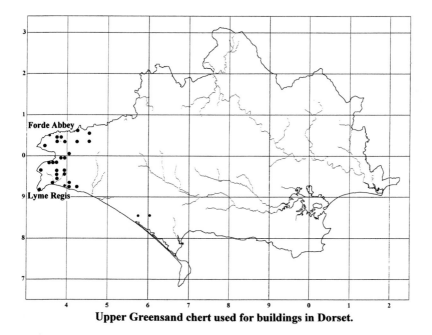

Upper Greensand chert used for buildings in Dorset.

to the steep sides of the Upper Greensand hills, where they have a dry footing in the Chert Beds. Chert is similar to flint, but tends to be lighter in colour, often a silvery blue or light tan, and is sugary rather than glassy in texture. All the hills had pits where the Chert was dug, either for road or building stone. The Iron Age forts of Pilsdon Pen, Lamberts Castle and Coneys Castle were built from hard chert cobs found on the summits, and the remains of later pits can still be seen on Blackdown.

Hardown Hill at Morecombelake has a necklace of pits in the Chert Beds below the top of the hill, and there are adits running into the hill. The cobs (pieces of chert) were so hard that they needed to be held inside wet sacks for hammering into useable pieces, while workmen wore wire safety goggles to avoid sharp chips damaging the eyes. Once loaded on a sled to go down the hill, the chert was taken as far as Exeter for road-making, and as a local building material for both cottages and churches it can be seen in Charmouth, Morecombelake, Whitchurch Canonicorum and a delightful little church at Catherston Leweston (1857). Here silvery grey chert has

Three examples of the use of Chert.
Top Cobbles of Chert and Lower Lias limestones gathered on Charmouth beach are used for garden walls and cottages in the village.
Centre The cobs of Chert from Hardown Hill are roughly split to give a smooth face to the wall of Charmouth church.
Bottom At Catherston Leweston the cobs of Chert have been split and fitted closely together as polygonal walling.

been selected and fitted closely together as polygonal walling, rather than in the neat horizontal lines more usual during the nineteenth century. The ancient church at Stanton St. Gabriel was built almost entirely of chert cobs from Hardown. Several pits are still open, and used in repairing historic buildings: one can be seen by the roadside at Fishpond below Lamberts Castle, another after a steep climb up Hardown Hill.

Stone used for building was not always quarried, but was merely collected from the fields. An example of this could be seen during the renovation of Bettiscombe Manor, below Pilsdon Pen. While drainage trenches were being dug next to the house it was possible to see that some of the doggers (rounded sandstone boulders) from the Thorncombe Sands of the hill above had been cut into blocks to provide foundations for the bricks which form the outer shell of the Manor. The bricks were made from the Middle Lias clays in a kiln in the field nearby.

JUNCTION BED On the eastern edge of the Marshwood Vale the Middle Lias clays and silts are topped by the Junction Bed limestone, so named because it is the junction between the Middle and Upper Lias. The Bed has two distinct parts, the lower being an iron rich oolitic marlstone which may have formed as an off-shore sand bank near the mouth of a river. As the chemistry of the water changed, iron which had been dissolved in river water could precipitate out and coat the sand grains in the same way that calcite coated the ooliths in limestone. The upper part is a mottled pink and white limestone, in which limestone which had almost hardened has been burrowed by shallow water marine animals, worn away and built up again several times.

There were quarries on each patch of limestone, though it was more often burnt for lime than used in building, as it contains many fossils, and is variable in strength. In Symondsbury the centre of the village is built on the Junction Bed, providing firm foundations. Some pieces of it can be seen in the walls of the farm buildings east of the church. Junction Bed limestone was quarried for building stone between Netherbury and Bowood, but the only remains of a large quarry are the stone sides of a field north of the footpath.

More patches of Junction Bed limestone can be found north of the Sherborne to Yeovil road, and part of the central area of Nether Compton also uses it as a foundation. It was quarried at Trent and Sandford Orcas, where the stone is white, and some pieces contain small ammonites. The medieval church at Trent has several blocks full of ammonites, said to come from a quarry in Church Fields which has unfortunately been ploughed over. Garden walls at Sandford Orcas Manor have pieces of Junction Bed limestone, quarried from Spillers Lane.

The Priest's house, or Chantry, Trent, was built of local
Junction Bed limestone in about 1500.

Wanderwell Quarry, Bothenhampton, in 1913, with its owner,
W. J. Cooper, wearing the straw boater on the right.

BURTON BRADSTOCK TO BROADWINDSOR

The cliffs to the west of Burton Bradstock are the Bridport Sands
(Upper Lias), a series of soft sands and thin bands of sandstone. The
soft sands, fine and even grained, have been used in the past for
mortar. The sand was mixed with lime from the two limestones
quarried on either side of the village. On the clifftop hill were
quarries in the Inferior Oolite, a stone which can still be seen in the
road cutting, and by the side of the garage. It is orange to cream in
colour, with beds up to 1 metre thick. It is fine grained and while
some beds contain many fossils, or dark brown iron-rich discs known
as 'snuff-boxes', the thicker and smoother beds have been used for
building stone.

On the hill to the north of Burton Bradstock were several quarries
in the Forest Marble limestone. Further west on the same hill, south
of Bothenhampton, the quarries were large, and their remains now
form the Wanderwell Nature Reserve. East of Burton Bradstock on
the Bredy road a Forest Marble quarry was working during the
nineteenth and early twentieth centuries.

[25]

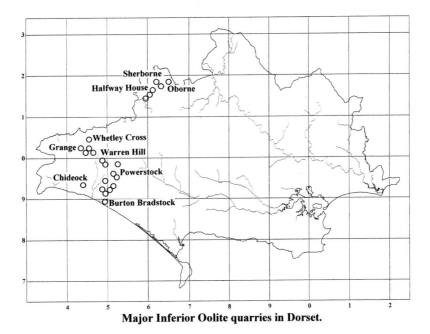

Major Inferior Oolite quarries in Dorset.

INFERIOR OOLITE From Burton Bradstock northwards through Beaminster to Drimpton, and Chideock eastward to Powerstock there were 138 quarries in the Inferior Oolite, in a total of 20 parishes. The limestone is usually found on the tops of small hills, and all the village buildings were originally of stone from their own parish quarries. Nineteenth century records show that the stone was taken further afield from some of the bigger quarries, for instance the accounts for the two Waddon Hill quarries list customers as far away as Thorncombe and Burton Bradstock. Salway Ash church was built free of charge from Waddon Hill stone, and everyone gave their labour and waggons for the community. At one time there were five limekilns on the hill, but only one was working in living memory. It would burn for six months non-stop: each winter the villagers gathered for a 'badger' feast as there was room under cover in the warmth for at least 50 people. They brought fresh bread which they heated on the kiln, as well as cider and meat. In the 1930s there were 24 men on piece-work for roadstone.

The quarries in this area are usually less than 4 metres deep, as the building stone beds are only about 2 metres thick, the rubbly beds above being used for limeburning. Most of the Inferior Oolite quarries could provide large enough blocks to be cut as ashlar, so that the manor house, church and vicarage of a village would be built of the best stone in ashlar, while the cottages were of dressed stone, and the farm buildings were rubble. Waste stone was burnt for lime, or used as roadstone. Successive maps surveyed over a period of time can show how quarries were worked across a particular hill. At Grange in Burstock the earliest maps show the quarry at the western end of the hill, later ones show it working eastward. In living memory the remaining limestone was used as roadstone. Most of the maps, and all of the few original written records refer to nineteenth century quarrying, so that the earlier history of the quarries must be found in the buildings.

A Roman camp on Waddon Hill would have used the Inferior Oolite which can still be seen in the farm quarry at Stoke Knap. There is some evidence of Saxon stone churches, most of which were replaced by the Normans, who also built castles, including one at

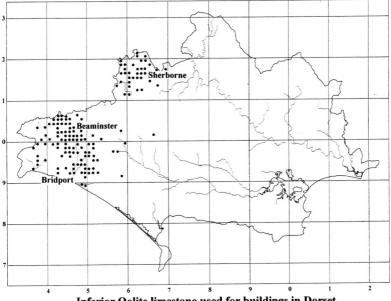

Inferior Oolite limestone used for buildings in Dorset.

Chideock. The quarry on Allington Hill was worked out during the eighteenth century, but was used for the thirteenth century hospital of St. Mary Magdalen and local cottages in the sixteenth and seventeenth centuries. The Victorians rebuilt many village churches, often re-using the original stone, but also newly quarried local stone. The best was said to come from Whetley Cross, Horn Park and Barrowfield, but the earlier large quarries of Grange and Chideock may have been quarried out by then. The east wall at Loders church came from Chiselcombe quarry on the northern side of the road at Loders Cross. This was the parish quarry during the nineteenth century, and the repair is recorded in the parish records.

Specifications in the Dorset Record Office refer to six cottages built for the Pymore Mill Co. in Loders in 1858 for £326., which included 146 loads of Mangerton stone at 2s 6d a load, and 154 hogsheads of lime from Mangerton or Beaminster at 1s 4d. Stone from Mangerton (Inferior Oolite) or Bothenhampton (Forest Marble) was specified for vaults and manholes; Mangerton for walls; Keinton Stone (Blue Lias from Keinton Mandeville, Somerset) for external doorways and steps; Bothenhampton stone for paving privies and courtyards; Bangor (Wales) slates for the roofs. Most of the factory complex and its associated cottages and school are of Inferior Oolite, though the 1843 warehouse has Bothenhampton stone outside and Loders (Inferior Oolite) on the inside. The mill complex is in Bradpole parish, but the whole of this area was dependent on the rope and net industry and many workers cottages show a similar style of building during the prosperous years of the early nineteenth century. In Loders, Bradpole and Allington there are cottages of Inferior Oolite with brick window and door reveals. (For an example of Inferior Oolite see the cottage at Symondsbury on the back cover.)

WEYMOUTH LOWLANDS FROM BOTHENHAMPTON TO FLEET

FOREST MARBLE In the Bridport area the Forest Marble limestone was quarried at Bothenhampton (known locally as Baunton). The beds of shelly limestone are only about 3cm thick in the upper part

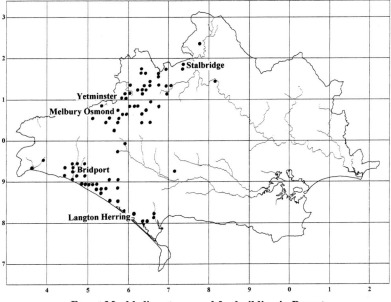

Forest Marble limestone used for building in Dorset.

of the deposit, but thicken to almost a metre lower down. The thin beds have been used for roofing, and the thickest ones cut for ashlar. Other beds have produced rubble, dressed stone and paving slabs. A small quarry can still be seen at Bothenhampton by following the footpath eastwards along the ridge of Wych Hill.

Forest Marble was also dug from a series of quarries east of Burton Bradstock towards Swyre and Bexington. The majority of the Formation consists of clays and thin sandstones, with the shelly limestone used for building occurring about half way through the sequence and only in isolated patches. The quarries are therefore not so numerous as the Inferior Oolite quarries, but tend to be deeper, as the limestones are in thicker deposits. The grey coloured stone is particularly strong and impervious because shell fragments are cemented together with crystalline calcite, leaving no pore spaces for the water to penetrate. The beds are of varying thickness and drape over each other where the current on the sea bed pushed banks of broken shells one over another. Under the great pressure of overlying rocks, in the millions of years since they were deposited, some of the shells dissolved and eventually re-crystallised as calcite. Being a better quality stone, it has been carried further from the source quarries than the Inferior Oolite. In Symondsbury, Loders and Bradpole the Forest Marble has been used as a foundation course or plinth, to prevent damp rising into the walls of Inferior Oolite above.

The houses and rope factories in Bridport are built almost entirely of Forest Marble, though the church was built of Inferior Oolite. Nineteenth century building specifications call for 'Baunton' stone for cellars and flooring, as well as bridges and walls by the river. Earlier Forest Marble masonry is not recorded in writing, but can be seen in the buildings themselves, as far afield as Bettiscombe, Beaminster, Charmouth, and Whitchurch Canonicorum.

Puncknowle, Swyre and Bexington had their own Forest Marble quarries and these villages have the typical grey look of that limestone. In the Bride valley building materials include Chalk block and flint, with Forest Marble from Burton Bradstock, Swyre or Puncknowle, Portland and Purbeck limestone from Portesham, and Corallian limestone which was quarried at Baglake Farm.

Langton Herring had three Forest Marble quarries which can be seen as 'waste' on a pre-1762 map showing the strip fields before enclosure. A fourth one appears on the tithe map of 1837, and all are shown on the Ordnance Survey map of 1880. Although these were not such deep quarries as those at Uplyme *The Dorset County Chronicle* reported in 1859 that Richard Carter was killed by a fall of stone in the quarry at Langton Herring. At West Fleet a quarry in the Forest Marble provided stone for Moonfleet house and its garden walls, as well as for the fifteenth century parish church.

CORNBRASH Most of the Cornbrash limestone was quarried for limeburning, but at the base of the Formation there is a massive blue-hearted limestone suitable for building. Cornbrash limestone from the Fleet and Chickerell quarries was used in the old village of Chickerell for houses as well as field walls. The church has an example of stone being used 'out of bed'. A Victorian addition on the north side has blocks of Cornbrash built with the face of the bed vertical, which have lasted barely 150 years, whereas in the older part of the building, the blocks of Cornbrash in the 1722 porch were built

The fifteenth century chancel of the old church at Fleet. The walls are Forest Marble limestone, the roof of heavy slabs of Forest Marble siltstone.

in the direction in which they were originally lying, and are still in good condition. The remains of a Cornbrash limestone quarry can still be seen next to the road at East Fleet, where the stone was used for East Fleet Farm.

CORALLIAN The Corallian Group is a series of sedimentary cycles of clays, sands and limestones, each representing the gradual retreat of sea level on the continental shelf, in which the clays were formed in deep water, the sands in shallower water as the sea began to retreat, and the limestones in the shallowest water at the end of the sequence. The cream to orange coloured limestones have been used for building, their most obvious characteristic being the oolitic texture. The ooliths are easily visible and form the greater part of the rock.

In the area between Chesil Beach and the Chalk Downs, the Corallian limestone has been used in Abbotsbury where the cottages are a patchwork of cream and white. The white stone is from Portesham quarry, which has produced thick blocks of stone of the same age as

Many of Abbotsbury's cottages are built of cream Corallian limestone, with a few white 'patches' of Portesham stone.

Portland stone, and thinner blocks of Lower Purbeck limestone. The cream is Corallian Abbotsbury Oolite, which has been given other local names such as the Todber Freestone and Osmington Oolite.

Geological sections of beds studied in north and south Dorset differ in detail, showing that conditions on the sea bed at the time of deposition were variable, but the most important building stones show a similarity in that the Todber Freestone and Abbotsbury Oolite are limestones with a fine grained powdery texture between the ooliths in the upper beds, and crystalline calcite in the lower, best-quality, bed. At Abbotsbury the upper beds, from the evidence of the buildings, have few ooliths, whereas at Todber the upper beds are as rich in ooliths as the lower. Also at Abbotsbury there seem to be more fossils in the stone. The building stone was originally quarried from Linton Hill, and possibly Chapel Hill for the Benedictine Abbey, but has been re-used in the village houses after the Dissolution of the Monasteries. Only the great barn (1400), St. Catherine's Chapel (late fourteenth century) and a few ruins survive.

The Abbotsbury Ironstone, which underlies the village and part of the hill to the north, is a deep rusty brown oolitic sand, rich in the iron mineral chamosite. In the nineteenth century a company was set up to exploit the ironstone, but it was found to contain too much sand. In the meantime sufficient planning had gone into the scheme for a railway to be built, and there was even a suggestion of an overhead conveyor to take the ore out to Chesil Beach to be loaded into boats. The railway was later used to carry stone from Portesham quarry, and shale from adits in the Kimmeridge Clay below.

The outcrop of Corallian limestone on Linton Hill extends eastward, so that Rodden and Langton Herring also have buildings of Corallian limestones from their own quarries.

Wyke Regis and the old part of Weymouth are built on the high ground of the Corallian Group. Sandsfoot Castle has lost most of its ashlar exterior, but the remaining rubble core is taken from the local cliffs of Osmington Oolite and the fossil-rich *Trigonia Clavellata* Beds. Like Abbotsbury, Osmington Oolite has more fossils than at Todber, but at Sandsfoot it is more grey than cream.

SHERBORNE AREA

In the Sherborne area limestones from the Inferior Oolite, Fullers Earth Rock and Forest Marble have been used for building, and sandstone from the Forest Marble Formation for paving.

INFERIOR OOLITE Between Nether Compton and Bradford Abbas 21 small quarries in the Inferior Oolite were shown on nineteenth century Ordnance Survey maps. The Compton quarries produced a good quality stone which is a deep rich orange when fresh, but weathers to a dark brown. Known as the Halfway House Bed, this limestone is ironstained and becomes more massive towards its base. Compton House has used the stone as ashlar, while the stables are of dressed stone. Lower in the same quarries there is a paler brown limestone which is blue hearted. This was used in the wall of the graveyard in Stallen, where it has been face-bedded (built with the face of the stone vertical). With only the blue colour visible, the first impression is of Blue Lias, but it can be seen on close inspection to be

A nineteenth century quarry of Inferior Oolite can still be seen
in Quarr Lane, Sherborne, and is today protected as a
Regionally Important Geological Site.

Cottages in Bristol Road, Sherborne, built of Inferior Oolite from Quarr Lane.

a sandy limestone rather than the fine powdery texture of Blue Lias.
The parishes of Over Compton, Trent, and Clifton Maybank also
used stone from the Compton quarries.

On the evidence of the village and local farm buildings the stone
quarried at Bradford Abbas is lighter and more mottled in colour

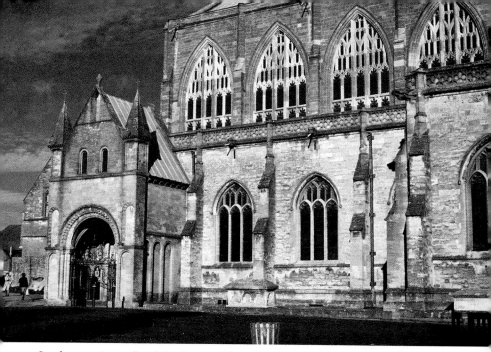

On the exterior walls of Sherborne Abbey the Inferior Oolite is paler than the stone from Ham Hill. It is also a fine, powdery limestone whereas the Ham Hill Stone is packed with broken shells.

than at Compton. Recent investigations on the evolution of the ammonites of the Inferior Oolite have revealed that there were up to 2000 quarries or scrapes in this area providing limestone. The soil is thin, with the solid limestone only inches below the surface. Most of the quarries have been worked out, but it is possible to see the beds of limestone in the railway cutting east of Bradford Abbas.

SHERBORNE BUILDING STONE Immediately north of Sherborne, from the Marston Road eastwards, the Inferior Oolite thickens dramatically. Here it is known as the Sherborne Building Stone and has formed into thick beds of pale cream limestone with only a few beds containing fossils. The remains of huge quarries can still be seen in Sandford Lane and Quarr Lane. In the fifteenth century a quarry by the Newell stream, close to the present hospital, was used to build St. John's Almshouse near the Abbey.

Sherborne is an excellent example of a predominantly one-stone town, built of Inferior Oolite, except for the Abbey and the ruins of the old Castle. The Abbey has a good deal of Ham Hill Stone on the outside and a collection of other stones inside. The Ham Hill Stone is darker brown than the Inferior Oolite, consisting of broken shell material surrounded by a sandy limestone coloured by iron, rather than the powdery limestone, with less iron, of the Inferior Oolite. In the thirteenth century Purbeck Marble was used for shafts in the Lady Chapel and the Abbots' tombs. Most of the shafts were replaced with Forest Marble from Lillington in the early twentieth century, but one Purbeck Marble shaft remains. To find it, look for the shaft with tiny whorls of snails, with sections cut across in many different directions. The Forest Marble shafts have broken shells whose original shape was probably that of an oyster, and Forest Marble was also used in the thirteenth century window shafts in Bishop Rogers Chapel, and in the more recent steps to the altar. The Forest Marble used in Sherborne prior to the nineteenth century is thought to have come from Highmore's Hill. The vaulting of the nave and choir roofs are of Tufa, which may have come from the stream running past the Castle. Blue Lias from Keinton Mandeville, Somerset, was laid in the nineteenth and early twentieth centuries on the floor of the ambulatory, the Lady and Bow chapels and the steps at the south and west entrances.

FULLERS' EARTH ROCK South of Sherborne the Terrace playing fields are on a natural terrace of the Fullers' Earth Rock, a wedge of limestone in the middle of the Fullers' Earth Clay, occurring in Dorset only in this area. The terrace runs from the old Castle to south west of Thornford. The fossils in the Fullers' Earth Rock include several distinctive brachiopods (a marine animal with two shells, but different from a bivalve). The stone is blue-hearted or pale cream and does not weather as well as the Inferior Oolite, but it has been used for several farm buildings in Thornford and Beer Hackett. The old quarry at Trill Farm which provided much local building material is now used as a sewage plant.

The old Castle at Sherborne is built on the same terrace. Bishop Roger of Caen was Bishop of Salisbury and Abbot of Sherborne. He may have brought Caen stone from Normandy to Dorset in the

The rubble filling of the walls of Sherborne Old Castle are of
Fullers' Earth Rock dug from the moat.

twelfth century, as there is a small amount in Wimborne Minster, but
the Norman stonemasons would have soon recognised good local
material. A moat was dug and the Fullers' Earth Rock used for
the inner core of the walls. Much of the ashlar which would have
covered this has been removed, but a Ham Hill stone column can
still be seen. Additional Inferior Oolite stone is recorded as coming from the Bishop's quarries at Combe, Sherborne. Some Forest
Marble shelly limestone can be recognised in a chevron pattern on an
inner wall. The 'new' Castle built by Raleigh during the reign of
Elizabeth I may also have used Fullers' Earth Rock, but it has been
rendered over. His house forms the core of the present building, with
wings and additional turrets added by the Digby family in 1625. The
stable block clearly shows different phases of building in the material
which has been used. Although the courtyard façade is all of Ham
Hill Stone, the outer walls of the early part (eighteenth century) are
of Inferior Oolite, and of the later part (nineteenth century) are of
Forest Marble, both of which were quarried on the estate.

East of Sherborne there were several quarries at Crendle and
Tripps Farm near Purse Caundle. Tripps Farm is entirely built of the
Fullers' Earth Rock, and it can also be seen in some of the walls at
Purse Caundle Manor. In common with most old buildings, different
builders have used all the stones available within a day's journey,
including Inferior Oolite, Forest Marble and Corallian limestones.

FOREST MARBLE AND CORNBRASH In this area the main limestones used for building are the Jurassic Forest Marble and Corallian, with a small amount of Cornbrash. From Halstock, through Yetminster and Longburton to Stalbridge, the Forest Marble Formation includes clay, siltstones and shelly limestones. Yetminster has been built of both Forest Marble and Cornbrash. Forest Marble is easily identified as it is packed with broken shell material. The Cornbrash used for building is a smooth limestone with a faint pink tone, some blocks having a few scattered fossils. The Forest Marble often contains small patches of orange clay, a characteristic which can also be seen in the cottages of Leigh and Chetnole, suggesting that their stone came from Yetminster quarry. The parish quarry was at Quarr Close, where according to ancient custom 'it is lawfull for the tennants to dig and to carry away at all times such stone as they shall need to build or repair their houses'.

The cottages in Longburton are all built of Forest Marble limestone and several other villages used stone from the same quarry. The oldest quarry was on the eastern side of the road, to the north of the village. The western one was only opened this century, and a great deal of stone was crushed to create a runway at a nearby airfield during the Second World War. Fields named on the Tithe map of 1843 as Quarry Ground and Limekiln Ground, north of the village, were probably part of a group of quarries on Lillington Hill which provided building stone, roadstone and lime. Holy Trinity church at Leweston School was built from these quarries in 1616.

In Sherborne and Yetminster both Forest Marble shelly limestone and Ham Hill Stone have been cut for use as roofing tiles. From the ground it is difficult to tell the difference, but a broken edge should show the colour: Forest Marble limestone is dark grey, Ham Hill Stone is orange. Like Ham Hill Stone, the shell fragments in Forest Marble are all lying flat and packed tightly together. However, the fragments of shell are larger and include bivalves, brachiopods, gastropods and crinoid plates (circular, up to 3cm diameter, with a

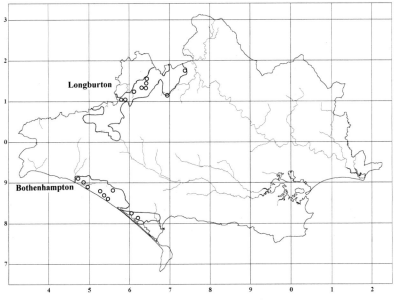

Forest Marble Formation outcrop and major quarries.

hole in the middle, or star shaped). The dark grey colouration is caused by the darker shells, in contrast to the orange caused by the presence of oxidised iron in the Ham Hill Stone.

A fine sandstone from the Forest Marble Formation has also been used for roofing tiles, and for setts in the pavement at the eastern end of the Sherborne Abbey precinct. These were brick-shaped cut pieces of stone turned on edge, so that the wear was taken across the grain of the stone and there was less danger of the road becoming slippery. The road cutting on West Hill, on the Dorchester road out of Sherborne, has crags of this sandstone on the eastern side. Thinner beds can be seen lower down the hill. It was quarried previously on this ridge and has been used also for setts in Shaftesbury and Southampton.

The Cornbrash limestone is rarely used for building, since it tends to be rubbly, but the lowest bed is massive and strong enough for use in buildings at Stalbridge and Yetminster. Several quarries have been dug through both the Cornbrash and Forest Marble, though in many cases the Cornbrash was only used for lime burning. Cornbrash is

Seniors Farm, adjoining Marnhull churchyard, shows the superior quality of Marnhull Corallian limestone.

generally cream coloured, but in different locations the building stone bed has been described as faintly blue, or pink.

In Stalbridge most of the listed buildings are of Cornbrash, whereas the later Victorian buildings are of Forest Marble. There are several small Forest Marble quarries in the parish, including one at Stalbridge Weston, but the largest still visible is in Henstridge. The wall round the manor estate has been built of stone from the nearest quarry, so that it changes character on the way round. Accounts of the sale of stone from Stalbridge quarries, both Cornbrash and Forest Marble, between 1780 and 1854, are lodged in the Dorset Record Office, in the papers of the Marquess of Anglesey.

CORALLIAN LIMESTONE In the northern part of the Blackmore Vale the most important quarrying has been in the Corallian limestones, since these are of the best quality for building. The best quality freestone (Todber Freestone) was quarried at Marnhull, where the quarry was mentioned in a survey of the possessions of Glastonbury Abbey after the Dissolution of the Monasteries, and the stone could have been carried on flat-bottomed barges down the

River Stour, as far south as Stourpaine. In the quarries still working at Todber, the beds can be seen to drape over one another as if they were sand banks being moved by a marine current towards the south-east. Between Marnhull and Todber several large quarries in the Todber Freestone have been in use since medieval times and possibly earlier, as Roman remains have been found there. Those nearest to Marnhull produced a fine oolitic freestone which can now be seen in buildings throughout the Stour valley. This stone, known to quarrymen as Marnhull stone, is almost white and free of fossils. Other beds in those same quarries, and most of the beds nearer Todber have been mottled by iron staining. Gannets quarry had 12 limekilns in 1918, and had a County Council contract for roadstone during the 1920's and 1930's, when it was still worked by hand, though the stone was collected by lorries. In the 1950's mechanical excavators came into use, and quarrying continued on a small scale until the recent boom in house-building has called for the traditional stone to be used in conservation areas such as Abbotsbury. With no Inferior Oolite being quarried at present, it has even been used in

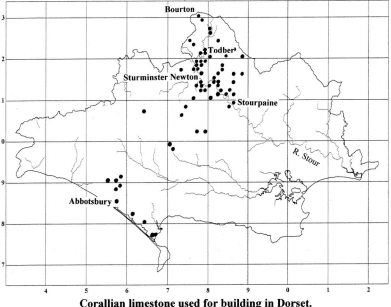

Corallian limestone used for building in Dorset.

Hammoon Manor is a fine example of well-cut ashlar from Marnhull.

Broadwindsor and Beaminster, as its colour almost matches.

The Todber Freestone thins and dies out both north and south, so that other villages use limestones from different parts of the Corallian Group. Cucklington Oolite, which was deposited earlier, is dark brown in colour, and was quarried north of Marnhull at Great Down Lane and on the hill above Buckhorn Weston. It can be recognised in many of the northern villages. Most of the houses in Marnhull, Stour Provost and Hinton St. Mary are built of dressed stone, only a few important houses have used the best stone as ashlar. The delightful Tudor manor house at Hammoon is one example, and the elegant Hanford House (1604-23) another. In Sturminster Newton there are many houses of Corallian limestone, but the church (1400, restored 1820's) is built of Upper Greensand from Shaftesbury. The town has been built on a bluff of Corallian limestone, and in the nineteenth century the Great Western Railway cut through almost all of the Corallian beds to carry the line through the town from one part of the river valley to the other. At Sturminster Mill the river turns a right angle, from north/south to an easterly direction. The mill building is of Corallian limestone and brick, on an Upper Greensand foundation. The Upper Greensand is better able to withstand erosion by water, and has also been used for the medieval bridge leading into the town.

The settlement of Newton, south of the river, had its own quarries and the buildings here are of noticeably coarser stone. At Fifehead Neville quarry there was about 2 metres depth of building stone similar to the stone at Newton, a coarse-grained cream coloured limestone with occasional fossils.

THE ISLES OF PORTLAND
AND PURBECK

The quarries on the islands of Portland and Purbeck are the most famous of all in Dorset, and their products can be found not only all over England, but in many overseas cities and war cemeteries. The limestones quarried there, and in the mainland quarries on the Ridgeway north of Weymouth, have been given the names of their localities here in Dorset, being considered as reference sections for rocks of the same age all over the world. The Ridgeway quarries were dug into both the Portland Limestone and the lower Purbeck limestones, so that Portesham stone for instance may be from either Formation. Historical records of buildings often use the name of the quarry, rather than the geological age of the stone when describing building materials. On the Isle of Portland most of the quarries are in the Portland Limestone only, except for Tout quarry, which also has lower Purbeck limestone available. The Isle of Purbeck quarries are distinguished from one another by the local terms 'inland' for the Purbeck Limestone, and 'cliff' for the Portland limestone. However, historians use the term 'Purbeck' for both.

PORTLAND LIMESTONE FORMATION The lower part of the Portland Limestone Formation contains a great deal of chert and is therefore only used for roadstone. Many quarries on Portland, and Swanworth quarry in Purbeck, still produce roadstone. The Freestone Series of the Portland Limestone has been quarried in three areas of Dorset; on the Ridgeway running from Portesham to Poxwell; on the Isle of Portland; and in the Isle of Purbeck. The Freestones have different characteristics in the three quarrying areas. On the Ridgeway the stone is a fine grained chalky white limemudstone formed in a quiet lagoon. At the time when the Portland

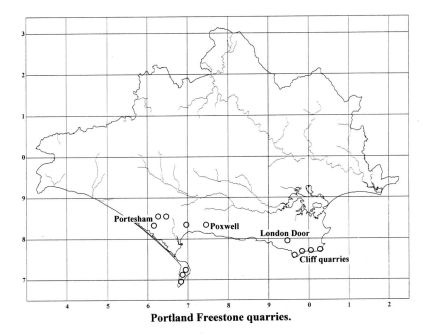

Portland Freestone quarries.

Beds were forming, the island area was very shallow and wave-swept, where oolith shoals were surrounded by algal reefs. The oolith shoals became the main freestone beds. To the east, in what is now the Isle of Purbeck, a slightly deeper shelf sea has also produced several beds of white oolitic freestone.

PURBECK LIMESTONE The beds of limestone within the Purbeck Limestone Group, with intervening softer beds of marl, shale and clay, formed in a series of shallow brackish and freshwater lagoons. The Lower Purbeck environment was a shallow water area where microscopic brackish-water shellfish known as ostracods (*Cypris*) lived, and the limestones contain large numbers of their fossils. Two periods of land-based deposits are represented by Dirt Beds with the remains of trees. Limestones of the Middle and Upper Purbeck Beds contain many freshwater fossils, though the Cinder Bed in the Middle Purbeck Beds is a thick bed of oysters which shows that the sea covered the area for part of the time. Because these beds were deposited in shallow lagoons they are not all laterally continuous.

Individual beds may thin out and disappear, or they may split into two or more layers of limestone so that from one quarry to another the precise details will be different. The quarrymen in the Isle of Purbeck, with hundreds of years of inherited experience, are able to identify a piece of stone from a specific quarry.

Purbeck limestones have been quarried in the past in two areas of Dorset. The Lower Purbeck limestones, in particular the Slatt and the *Cypris* Freestones, were dug in many quarries from Portesham to Upwey and in the Poxwell area. South of Bincombe the limestones were mined underground on Green Hill, west of the Coombe Valley. The building stone quarries in the Isle of Purbeck today, and the mines of previous centuries are in the Middle Purbeck. In the Upper Purbeck the Broken Shell limestone, known as the Burr to quarrymen and masons, was cut as ashlar and can be seen in the remains of many medieval buildings. The three Marble beds are the highest beds in the Upper Purbeck, and have been used mostly for interior work.

THE RIDGEWAY QUARRIES – PORTESHAM TO POXWELL

The largest part of Portesham Quarry is in the Lower Purbeck beds, but some limestone has been dug from three beds of Portland limestone, the highest of which contains oyster shells, while the two below have very few fossils, though a large *Titanites giganteus* ammonite was found in the lowest bed recently. The Portland limestone is white, fine grained and chalk-like in appearance, and can be seen by the footpath to Portesham Farm. The white limestone used in Abbotsbury, some probably re-used from the Abbey, came from Portesham Quarry. There are three different types; a white laminated stone, chalky to sandy in appearance, the pieces approximately 8cm thick; a similar stone not laminated, tending to cream, with a sandy texture and up to 12cm thick; and a shelly limestone with shells approximately 5mm diameter tumbled in all directions, a pale cream colour, in blocks approximately 16cm square, or larger ashlar. This last stone was used for Hardy's Monument, on Blackdown Hill, and for Old Sheps cottage in Portesham. The first two limestones are from the Lower Purbeck beds at Portesham, the third

A seventeenth century cottage in Portesham. Portesham Quarry yielded
both thick Portland stone for ashlar, and thinner
Lower Purbeck for dressed stone.

from the Portland beds. The lowest bed of the Purbeck and the top
bed of the Portland Stone were quarried out in one block, but the
two separated cleanly and easily when hammered. The *Cypris* Freestones were dug from higher in the quarry, so that several beds of
useful stone were available throughout the depth of the excavation.
Portesham Quarry was large enough to supply stone beyond its
immediate hinterland, including the Tudor manor house at Athel-
hampton. In the nineteenth century stone was carried by rail to
Upwey, and the remains of a tramway down the hill can still be seen.
An 1889 advertisement in *The Dorset County Chronicle* quotes prices
for Portland and Purbeck stone, rock faced and smooth faced, or
lime, for delivery to all stations to Wareham, and to Paddington.

The ridge formed by the 'Portesham limestones' and the underlying
Portland Sand runs from Portesham past Waddon Manor (seventeenth & eighteenth centuries) and Corton Farm (sixteenth and
seventeenth centuries), both of which were built of stone from
Portesham or Friar Waddon quarries. Windsbatch Quarry near

Upwey Mill, an example of the Lower Purbeck *Cypris* Freestones.

Upwey church provided stone for the Tower of London in the reign of Edward III. The stone has a white chalky appearance, and weathers into thin laminations, with the very fine stringers of sand between beds of limestone weathering out, leaving a recess. All the historic buildings in Upwey and the local villages, as well as Dorchester, are of this type of stone. Woodsford Castle in the Frome valley was built of Lower Purbeck limestone in the fourteenth century. Excavations at Maiden Castle have found the footings of Iron Age buildings using stone from Upwey.

The stone from the Ridgeway quarries has been used in the upper Piddle valley, most noticeably in the churches, which have walls of dressed Lower Purbeck limestones and quoins, window mullions and doorways of the Portland Freestone ashlar. In the Cerne valley the Lower Purbeck is banded with flint in several churches and farmhouses. In the lower Piddle valley, Puddletown and Athel-hampton have been built of stone from these quarries, though in both the Piddle and Frome valleys stone from the Isle of Purbeck becomes more easily available downstream. The medieval bridge at Wool was considered to be an acceptable day's journey by horse and cart from Corfe Castle, and is the apparent boundary between the two sources.

Portland Roach shows the moulds of bivalve and gastropod fossils.

THE ISLE OF PORTLAND

The fine quality freestones from the Portland Limestone Formation have famously been used for public buildings throughout the world. The majority of the stone has come from the Isle of Portland itself, though there are also extensive cliff quarries in Purbeck where stone of the same age and comparable quality has been dug.

The shoal complex which formed in this shallow area of the sea has provided two even-textured oolitic freestones. The Whit Bed is a well-cemented oolite, and therefore the most valuable. The Base Bed is softer, more easily worked, but of poorer quality. A comparison between the two shows that the ooliths in the Base Bed are larger. On the other hand, the Whit Bed contains bivalve fossils, giving a slightly rougher appearance. On the edges of the oolite shoals patch reefs grew up, made of an alga (*Solenopora*) and oyster shells, and these have formed a distinctive limestone in the northern quarries.

Above these two is the Roach, an oolitic limestone in which the fossils have been dissolved out, leaving moulds and casts in the shape of the Portland Screw (a gastropod, *Aptyxiella portlandica*) and "osses 'eads" (two bivalves *Laevitrigonia* and *Myophorella*). The Roach will ring like a bell when struck, and has proved extremely strong, being used in the nineteenth century for harbour walls and fortifications. It is said to withstand the pounding of heavy artillery better than Cornish granite, and was used for the Nothe Fort (1850's) and Hurst Castle. My theory on its strength is that the energy of the cannon ball is dissipated by the holes in the Roach, whereas the interlocking crystals in granite would 'feel' the full force throughout the body of the stone. In earlier centuries the Roach was often left as waste material in the spoil heaps.

There are 36 named quarries on the Isle of Portland, including Perryfield, Broadcroft, Independent, Kingbarrow, Inmosthay and Shepherds Dinner. Several are still working to produce building stone, block stone for sea defences, headstones and memorials, and roadstone.

The Romans are believed to have used some stone from Portland, and Norman work using Portland Freestone includes part of Christchurch Priory, and the twelfth century Portland church of St. Andrew. There was intermittent use during the Middle Ages, including examples in Exeter (1303) and London (1340's). On Portland itself Rufus Castle was built in 1430, and the Bow and Arrow Castle (also fifteenth century) had quoins of the Cap, which is the thick bed at the base of the Purbeck Beds.

The introduction of frame-saws and water-power in the seventeenth century made it possible to cut larger blocks of stone, and Inigo Jones used Portland stone for the Banqueting Hall at Whitehall (1619). Wren used it for many churches in London after the Great Fire of 1666, and his most famous building, St. Paul's Cathedral, started in 1675, was built of stone from the Grove Quarries. The church of St. George at Reforne, on Portland was built of Roach in 1776. The list could lengthen indefinitely. In London the Goldsmiths Hall and the Reform Club, Greenwich Hospital, the British Museum (1753), Somerset House (1776), and many government buildings such as the General Post Office and Horseguards Parade (1829) all remain as proof of the old saying that more Portland has been carried away than remains on the Island. The Cenotaph, designed by Sir Edward Lutyens, was built of Portland stone in 1919, and many town and village war memorials follow the same pattern. Headstones in military cemeteries from both world wars were of Portland

Virtually all of Portland is built of Portland freestone quarried on the Island, as shown in this Fortuneswell cottage.

The Portland Stone War Memorial in Bournemouth.

A quarryman using a pneumatic drill to break out a block of
stone in a Portland quarry in the 1950s.

limestone, and they are continually being replaced. Modern buildings
of Portland Freestone can be found in London, Leeds, Southampton
and Manchester. Portland Freestone has also been exported overseas,
including America, where it was used for colonial buildings in Vir-
ginia, and for marking the Mason-Dixon line. Dublin's Georgian
elegance owes much to Portland Stone.

In Tout Quarry on Portland the lowest bed of Purbeck limestone,
the Hard Cap, contains algal mounds and fossil trees. It has been
quarried for building, though a great deal has been wasted because of
the trees. Above the Hard Cap, the Slatt consists of thin sheets of
limestone which have been used for roofing.

In Purbeck, the old cliff quarries in the Portland Freestone can still be seen under St. Aldhelm's Head, and at Winspit, East Man, Seacombe, Dancing Ledge and Tilly Whim, but many of the galleries are now collapsing under the weight of the overburden. West of St. Aldhelm's Head the Freestones thin and become cherty, and are unsuitable for building. In the old quarries still open in the cliffs, large oysters can be seen in the roof of the galleries, which are in the Under Freestone. The higher galleries were cut in the Pond Freestone, the lowest bed in the quarry still being worked inland of St. Aldhelm's Head. Both Freestones are shell-sand limestones with occasional oolitic layers, the Under being the coarser of the two.

The highest bed at St. Aldhelm's Quarry is the Shrimp Bed, a white, fine-grained, smooth lime-mudstone, in which shrimp-like fossils have been found. Underneath is the Titanites or Blue Bed which weathers to a greyish colour, is used for ornamental work and contains fossils of bivalves, as well as the huge ammonite *Titanites giganteus* measuring up to half a metre in diameter. The Spangle, underneath again, contains fossils which have been replaced by calcite crystals. When freshly cut it sparkles in the sunshine, and it has

The old cliff quarry workings at Winspit, on the coast near Worth Matravers, showing the entrance to the underground galleries.

often been used for window surrounds and sills in the Isle of Purbeck and Poole.

There were two quarries inland, at London Door and on the ridge above Kimmeridge, the latter being used for roadstone. The present working quarry at Swanworth is used only for roadstone, but there it is possible to see the whole of the Portland Limestone Formation, including the lower Cherty Series. On the eastern face of the quarry the lower Purbeck beds can be seen, though they are of no commercial value.

The quarries in the Isle of Purbeck may have been used earlier than those on Portland because they were easier to reach, though said to be harder to work. Galleries were cut horizontally into the cliff, taking advantage of the bedding planes and joints to allow blocks to be lifted out. The stone was shipped from the cliff quarries, a crane being fixed at the quarry to lower it on to a rock nearly level with the surface of the water, and another crane being used to load it into barges which carried it out to larger ships. Many historical records refer to Purbeck stone, but they are in fact Portland Freestone from

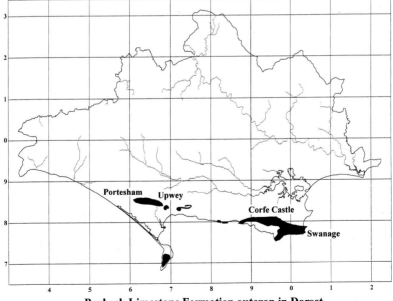

Purbeck Limestone Formation outcrop in Dorset.

The sixteenth century manor house at Kingston Maurward was built of Portland Stone from the cliff quarries in Purbeck.

the Isle of Purbeck. This has been known as Purbeck-Portland for many years. Kingston Russell house was built of Portland stone from the Isle of Purbeck in the mid seventeenth century. Other local buildings using Purbeck-Portland are Herringston (sixteenth century), the old manor house at Kingston Maurward (sixteenth century), Lulworth Castle (1608), Tyneham House (now demolished), Poxwell Manor (about 1618), Warmwell (about 1618) and Creech Grange (eighteenth century).

In the Purbeck Limestones most of the beds are thin, being separated by varying thicknesses of lime rich shale or clay. The beds used for building are in the middle of the Formation, with the Cinder Bed, rich in oysters, forming an easily recognised reference point. The New Vein is below the Cinder Bed, and the Downs Vein, Freestone Vein and Laning Vein above. Each bed contains different bivalve shell fossils, reflecting changing environments, and is either cream or grey according to the colour of the shells. The Downs Vein and the Freestone of the Freestone Vein are cream, containing shells of *Neomiodon*, approximately 0.5 centimetre across. These limestones originated as a shell-sand which hardened into rock in a warm, Mediterranean type climate. The Freestone Vein includes many named beds, such as the Roach, Thornback and Grub, containing the dark grey shells of oysters. These Middle Purbeck building stones are all quarried on the upper slope and top of the hill from Worth to Swanage. They were previously mined in underground galleries until this was forbidden for safety reasons.

The earliest workings followed the beds of rock underground from their outcrop on the southern slope of the hill facing the sea. By the seventeenth century, when the industry expanded, inclined shafts were driven from the top of the hill down through the thin limestones and shales to reach the building stone beds below. The inclines could be steeper, when less building up of the sides was necessary, but they averaged a 45 degree slope, with steps at one side for the men, and a paved slide at the other on which blocks of stone could be hauled to the surface.

Underground the quarrymen worked along the line of a vein of stone. There are several beds in each vein, one being left as a ceiling for the gallery or lane, another left as the floor. The clays between are too soft and would collapse. The ceiling was propped using timber supports with a stone on top which could be knocked out later. All the limestone beds have joints or cracks 60 or 90 centimetres apart, their thickness varying from a few centimetres to over 30. To remove a block the quarryman would drive his paddle – a steel bar with a chisel end – into the clay between the limestone beds. He would lever out the clay – known as underpicking – until he had cleared all the clay out from underneath the stone. The first piece on the floor would need both surfaces cleared, but those above could be removed using their own weight.

As the men often worked in lanes only a metre high, they could not stand upright, but crouched at their work, which helped provide balance when swinging a hammer to drive in the paddle. Blocks of stone were rolled onto small flat-bed carts made of elm, strengthened all round with iron plates. Small solid wheels were set close together underneath for manoeuvrability in the confined space underground. Loading the cart required judgement as to the slope of the lane, the bends which might have to be negotiated, and the size and thickness

Quarrymen outside their quarr house in about 1890. The donkey circled the capstan, which in turn pulled carts loaded with stone to the surface.

of the stone. The stone was fastened to the cart with chains fixed through eyes at either end and the sides, and the men pulled the cart, walking backwards with a chain round their hips. The carts were hauled up the incline by donkeys who walked round pulling a long wooden arm, or 'spack' attached to an elm capstan.

The top of the hill from Worth to Swanage, where most of the quarrying has been carried on from the seventeenth century to the present day, is apparently flat on the surface, but in fact the beds have been folded and broken by the pressure of continental movement, the push coming from the south. The folds are across the slope of the hill, the faults running north-west south-east. When a quarryman finds a weakness in a piece of stone which is aligned in this direction, he cannot cut across it, or it will fall apart.

The stone was cut to shape in open-sided quarr houses on the surface. Thin beds were set aside for roofing slabs, graded according to size, but only roughly cut at the sides. Thicker beds were sliced along the line of the bedding, cutting away the top and bottom and using the inner heart of the stone for paving, building, setts, or kerbs and guttering. A small amount of the darker beds which will take a polish were and still are used for headstones. The cut stone was stored in bankers at the quarry, to be carried down to Swanage

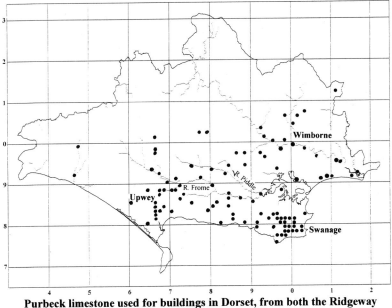

Purbeck limestone used for buildings in Dorset, from both the Ridgeway quarries and the Isle of Purbeck.

on large-wheeled wagons which could be backed into the sea. The stone was manhandled into small barges which went out to sea-going vessels anchored in deeper water. The stone was then winched aboard the larger vessel using a spar half-way up the mast.

Both historians and geologists have published descriptions of the Purbeck Limestone building stones. At either end of the Isle of Purbeck the beds can be seen at Worbarrow and in Durlston Bay. In Durlston Bay the beds can be seen to dip northwards, forming the slope of the hill, and the veins of building stone can be recognised, using the massive grey Cinder Bed as a reference point. This is about half way between Peveril Point and the zig zag path, in two thick beds which look like cinders from a coal fire.

Under the Cinder Bed (to the south) the New Vein, a massive cream limestone, includes beds such as the Brassy bed, Tombstone bed and Pudding bed, with a Feather bed above. Immediately below the Cinder Bed a limestone which has been quarried for building is named the Button Bed. The Cinder Bed is a massive bed of oysters, set in a mudstone. It is of no use for building, and nineteenth century historians said no tools could work it – "Gunpowder alone can affect it." Even today's machines have difficulty moving it, so most of the quarries stop above it.

Above the Cinder Bed (north) the Upper Building Stones commence with the Downs Vein which is a massive limestone nearly 1 metre thick, crowded with small bivalves. It can be split into slabs 8-10 centimetres thick and has been used mainly for paving, in London as well as Dorset. Thinner slabs up to 2 centimetres thick have been used as roofing tiles throughout the Isle of Purbeck. Some of the beds are known as Pond, Mangy or Clear-all. Above the Downs Vein are more limestones and shales, the next useful bed being the Laper, a thin limestone used for roofing.

The Freestone Vein includes the Blue Bed which is thinly bedded with sand-sized shell fragments, the Wetston Bed, the White Horse and the Dun Cow. The latter has limestone filled sun cracks on one surface and is used as a decorative stone. The Freestone is a thick bed which can be cut as ashlar as well as roughly dressed stone, and can be used 'out of bed' without splitting away. The manor house at Dunshay was one of the earliest to be built of Freestone, in 1642. The site of the Marble quarry which was used in the thirteenth century for Salisbury Cathedral is on the driveway to the Manor.

The fifteenth century Town Cellars in Poole are built of
Purbeck limestone with a little local heathstone.

The Freestone was used a great deal in the nineteenth century for churches in Poole and Bournemouth.

The Roach, Thornback and Grub from the Freestone Vein have been used for paving and occasionally slabs from these or New Vein have been thin enough for use as roofing tiles. The size of these tiles, when seen from inside a roof, is considerably larger than the limestone tiles used in West Dorset. They are not cut to size, but simply sorted so that the smallest are at the apex of the roof, the largest near the eaves. They may be as much as 90 centimetres long and 60 centimetres wide.

Apart from the bivalve shells which make up most of the building stones, the footprints of dinosaurs have been found on the surface of the limestone, and the bones, scales and teeth of fishes, turtles, crocodiles and mammals in the clay between. When working by hand, the quarrymen were able to save the best fossils and many are now in museums. All the veins of stone could be worked in separate galleries under a man's patch of land, while farming continued on the surface. The landowners were then able to charge royalties on the stone, as well as rent on the land. The removal of the strongest beds in the series has led in some places to subsidence of the land, so that much of it is not suitable for building. Open cast quarrying has been carried on since the last World War, since the invention of large earth-moving equipment. Deep pits are cut through all the limestones and shale, and several veins of building stone can be dug from the same hole. These pits can be seen near many footpaths throughout the Worth and Langton Matravers area, and show the full succession of cream coloured limestones and grey shales. Although scientifically important, they are not safe to visit, as the stone is loose and may fall at any time.

The Burr or Broken Shell Limestone and the Marble beds of the Upper Purbeck can be seen at Peveril Point. The double V of the reefs are the Marble beds, while the Burr is in two thick beds in the cliff. The Burr was quarried for ashlar in Norman times and the Middle Ages. It can be seen in Corfe Castle and the churches in Worth Matravers, Studland and Christchurch Priory. Henry VIII's fortification on Brownsea was built of Purbeck Burr limestone. In these older buildings centuries of weathering have brought out the difference from the Downs Vein and Freestone, for though all three

Beds of limestone and shale in the Middle Purbeck, from the Laning Vein down to the Freestone, in Queensground Quarry, Langton Matravers. The quarry is approximately 12 metres deep.

are cream coloured, the shells in the Burr are broken and tumbled in every direction, while the limestone matrix has weathered away into cavernous holes. This weathering is so characteristic that it is possible to recognise isolated pieces of Burr in the remains of medieval buildings at some distance from Purbeck, including Milton Abbey, the remains of the nunnery at Tarrant Crawford, and even one piece in the church at Whitchurch Canonicorum. The original Norman bridge south of Wareham (replaced in 1778, and rebuilt in the 1930s) was built of Burr, as was St. Martin's Saxon church. This stone was still being quarried until fairly recently, so that some of the pieces recognised may be repairs. It was even used for a rockery in the Pavilion gardens in Bournemouth, which seems a waste when it can be carved into beautiful shapes.

All the Marbles and the Burr were quarried in medieval times from Peveril Point along the northern slope of the Purbeck hill, from Swanage through Crack Lane, Quarr and Dunshay to Lynch. Three beds of Marble can be seen at Peveril Point. The blue is the one most commonly used in the slender columns in medieval churches, and the grave slabs of bishops or other notables, and it is easily recognised by the sections cut through the fossil gastropod, *Viviparus*. The red and green marbles also contain *Viviparus*, though more scattered,

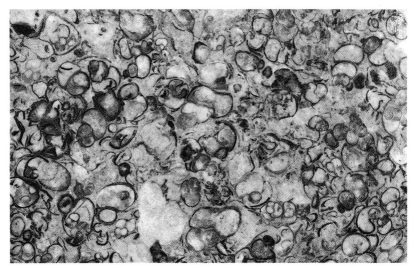

Purbeck Marble is recognisable by the infinitely variable sections cut across the *Viviparus* freshwater snail fossils.

with the addition of *Unio* (known as the devil's hoofprints) in the green, and are coloured by glauconite and other minerals. None of these stones are true marbles, but they can be polished, and retain their sheen when used for interior work. If allowed to weather outside, the limestone matrix dissolves away, leaving the whorls of the gastropod standing proud, and the outside of the stone turns to a yellow/cream colour. This can also happen inside a church, if the stone becomes damp.

The Romans used Purbeck Marble at Silchester and Verulamium (St. Albans), and the Saxons for fonts and grave-slabs. As a structural material, for columns and capitals, the Marble was popular in the Early English period. The earliest example may be in Wolvesey Palace at Winchester (about 1141). Many churches built between 1170 and 1350 have columns, carvings, fonts and effigies, including Salisbury (1258), Dublin, Exeter, Worcester, Durham, St. Albans, Winchester, Chichester, Westminster, and Wells. In Tarrant Crawford church are two graveslabs taken from the nearby Abbey, for Queen Joan of Scotland (died 1239) and Bishop Poore, who built Salisbury Cathedral and was born at Tarrant Crawford. Purbeck Marble graveslabs can be found in many places in Dorset, including Tarrant Rushton, Abbotsbury, and a green marble one at Whitchurch Canonicorum. Although not normally strong enough for building work, the Marble has been used for farm buildings near the quarries, including the foundations of the farmhouse at Quarr where its burial has preserved it from weathering. The Constable's House in Christchurch also has Marble on the outer wall, with other Purbeck limestones in the interior.

The Marble was taken to Corfe Castle for carving, and layers of marble chippings could be about three metres deep. In the thirteenth and fourteenth centuries some of the marblers moved to royal works set up in Westminster and London. Before the port of Swanage was developed in the early eighteenth century, the stone was shipped from Ower, within Poole Harbour, and an agreement dated 24th October 1695 gives the payment as a pound of pepper and a football, to be paid on Shrove Tuesday – a custom still celebrated today. The worked stone was taken from Corfe Castle along the present Studland road to just west of Higher Bushey Farm, then across Rempstone Heath to Ower. The bank where it was stored to await shipping is now the front lawn of the cottage. After 1400 the use of Marble declined, and there seems to have been little use of the stone during the next two hundred years, when Portland took precedence.

In 1651 the quarrymen set up the Company of Marblers in order to protect their interests and in 1698 there were 142 Freemen of the Company. The Company has been mostly restricted to the traditional quarrying families and Freemen were admitted at the age of 21. Many of the original families are still quarrying today, though the 200 Freemen in the early twentieth century are now considerably reduced.

Flat paving was used in the eighteenth and nineteenth centuries for flooring in houses and for pavements in cities such as London. Roadways which had to take greater wear from horses hooves and the wheels of carts were paved with setts. Several different beds were used indiscriminately, though the Grub and Thornback (rough like a Thornback skate) containing grey shells seem to predominate in those examples which survive today. Stone for building, paving, kerbstones and gutters was dressed to shape at the quarry. Much of the stone produced in Purbeck was shipped to London for paving, but it was also used for building the sea wall at Portsmouth. John Hutchins, the eighteenth century Dorset historian, records that 'Between June 1750 and September 1752 the trustees of Ramsgate Harbour employed 50 sail of vessels in transporting hence 15,000 tons of stone. . . After being brought down from the quarries in carts, the greater part of it is deposited on the shore or banks, and afterwards carried in high-wheeled carts into the sea, when it is transferred into boats, and by them conveyed to larger vessels.' He also mentions 'a red stone with which the pier at Ramsgate is built'. One the Marbles and one of the Rags are red.

Hutchins also records that in 1760 the price of 100 ft of paving stone, weighing one and three quarter tons was £1.13s. on board ship; a ton of pitchers (cobbles) 9s; and freight to London per ton 7s. Between January 1764 and January 1771 ninety four thousand tons were shipped from Swanage, or 270 tons a week. At this time there were 63 quarries in Swanage. In 1793 four hundred people were engaged in quarrying. Most were members of quarrying families who were self-employed, paying a royalty to the landowner. In the five years up to 1801 38,750 tons, mostly of flagstones, were shipped from Swanage for paving London. In the *Victoria County History of Dorset* it is recorded that in 1877 there were 92 mines, which produced 11,816 tons of dressed stone and 1,411 tons of undressed stone.

The change from the Jurassic marine sediments, which were laid down under constantly changing sea levels, to the Cretaceous era, which was more settled for a long period of time, is taken as being within the Purbeck Limestone Formation, which formed in brackish or freshwater lagoons as sea level was falling. The Marbles contain the fossils of freshwater snails, and are followed by the Wealden sands and clays. On the southern side of the Chalk ridge between Studland and Swanage, the sands and clays of the Wealden Formation form the valley between Swanage and Lulworth Cove. They were deposited in a large lake fed by rivers running from the west. Grains of minerals from the granite of Dartmoor are found in the Coarse Quartz Grit on the ridge across Corfe Common. This Grit was cut for use in a few of the farm buildings locally.

CENTRAL DORSET DOWNLAND

The central downland of Dorset is dominated by the Chalk, with the Upper Greensand appearing on the lower hill slopes. The Gault clay and Lower Greensand is found in a few places in the valleys.

UPPER GREENSAND In northern Dorset, the Shaftesbury Sandstone of the Upper Greensand is of excellent quality, and has been used mostly as ashlar. Shaftesbury Sandstone appears dark green, especially when wet, the green being an iron mineral, glauconite. Glauconite is a member of the mica mineral family, rich in iron but also containing potassium, magnesium and aluminium. It is usually

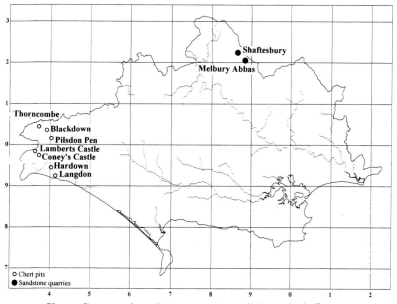

Upper Greensand sandstone quarries and chert pits in Dorset.

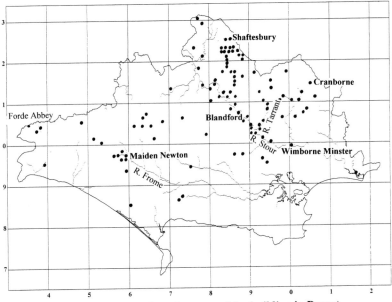

Upper Greensand sandstone used for building in Dorset.

On Gold Hill, Shaftesbury, the retaining wall has been built of Upper Greensand sandstone, blocks of which can be seen in situ half-way down the hill. The cobbles and houses are also of Greensand.

considered to indicate deposition under marine conditions when little land-based sediment was being deposited. The beds are a weakly cemented lower sandstone, with a hard shelly calcite-cemented glauconitic sandstone above. This upper bed, previously known as Ragstone, was quarried on both sides of the hilltop at Shaftesbury, where the quarries can still be seen near the footpath on Wilderness, in spite of their having been used as rubbish tips. The same sandstone was also quarried at Melbury Abbas and Compton Abbas, but the stone becomes too soft for building further south.

The Saxon town of Shaftesbury, on the western end of the hill, was built on the free-draining Chert Beds, fresh water being available from springs below the steep hillsides, or from wells dug only a few metres into the sandstone. The hill originally formed as the springs caused landslides over the clays below, undermining the sandstone. Loose boulders would have been gathered for building, as they have been in living memory. The Saxon abbey was built in 880 and it is possible that stone was quarried from the sides of the original hill. After the Dissolution of the Monasteries the abbey was demolished and the stone used for domestic buildings within the expanding town. A few carved blocks can be identified. Quarrying continued until 1888, two quarries being visible on a map of the town drawn by Upjohn in 1799.

Shaftesbury Upper Greensand has been used for building in all the villages around Shaftesbury, and has been carried down the Stour as far as Wimborne. Sturminster Newton church is entirely Shaftesbury Greensand. It is often used with other materials, such as flint at Ashmore, heathstone in the Tarrant valley, and Purbeck limestone further south.

CHALK The Chalk formed on the floor of an outer continental shelf sea, and consists of microscopic plate-like crystals of calcite forming hollow balls which were the skeletons of coccoliths (microscopic plankton). The lowest beds of the Chalk contain some glauconite, like the Upper Greensand beneath, and occasional sand grains with scattered fossils. Most of the Upper Chalk is too soft for building and contains few fossils. The Chalk is several hundred metres thick, providing beds of different texture, fossil and mineral content. Mostly white in colour, the lowest beds appear grey by contrast. The

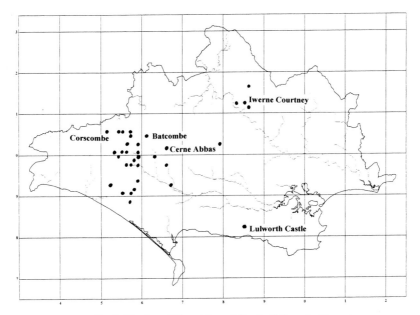

Chalk block or 'Clunch' used for buildings in Dorset.

Melbourn Rock at the base of the Middle Chalk, and the Chalk Rock and Top Rock in the Upper Chalk have been suggested as building stones. Pits on Melbury Hill and Compton Down include the Chalk Rock.

The vast majority of the hundreds of Chalk pits in Dorset have been quarried for roadstone or lime production and it is not possible to judge which, if any, of the present pits provided building stone. There are no written records of stone being used for building, except for a suggestion that a white stone from Melbury was used for some of the building at Eastbury House in Tarrant Gunville. This was designed in the eighteenth century by Vanbrugh to rival Blenheim Palace, and was built of Shaftesbury Upper Greensand and a calcareous sandstone from the Vale of Wardour known as Chilmark Stone. Most of the building was demolished in 1780, and any white stone has been lost.

The record of quarrying for Chalk blockstone can only to be seen in the surviving buildings of the villages around the edge or in the folds of the Downs, where the Chalk has been used in block form for

'Clunch' cottages in Cattistock have foundations of stronger stone.

house building. It is known as 'clunch', and has proved to be rather soft in some cases. At Hooke several of the Chalk buildings have been demolished and replaced by ones of Inferior Oolite.

At Cattistock many cottages have been rendered and of those left uncovered some are weathering badly. However, as usual, it depends on the quality of a particular piece of stone. As Chalk is porous, house walls are usually built on a plinth of less porous stone, such as flint, Forest Marble or Corallian limestones. At least two different ammonites can be seen in the 'clunch' wall of the Fox and Hounds, with a small echinoid spine. Blocks in other buildings contain scattered sand grains. At Sydling St. Nicholas the 'clunch' also looks sandy. At Cerne Abbas the vet's surgery, originally the fifteenth century North Barn of the Abbey, has been built of huge blocks of nodular Chalk containing random lumps of flint (possibly Middle Chalk). In the village dressed blocks of Chalk contain scattered grains of glauconite and occasional fossils of the spiral ammonite *Turrilites acutus,* all characteristic of the Lower Chalk.

FLINT Flint is present in much of the Chalk, but is concentrated in the Upper Chalk which forms the crest of many of the hills. It is a form of silica which has not crystallised, giving the impression of having originally been a jelly in separate lumps within the coccolith-mud of the Chalk when it was soft. In the Upper Chalk the neat

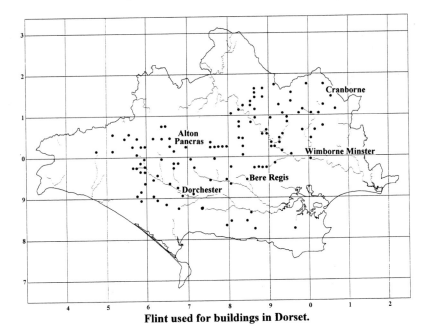

Flint used for buildings in Dorset.

horizontal lines of flint may be burrow-fills, but those more randomly distributed are often replacements of fossils such as sponges and echinoids. Being rounded, these two often survive in gravels formed by weathering of the Chalk.

Thousands of years of weathering have formed a superficial deposit known as Clay-with-Flints on top of the hills, and terrace gravels of broken flints are associated with many of the rivers. The flint used in building could therefore have been separated from the Clay-with-Flints when the clay was being prepared for brickmaking, dug specifically from the terrace gravels, or simply collected from the fields after ploughing.

The hardness of flint makes it a good building material, providing a weatherproof exterior or a strong core for a wall. However the uneven shape means that the structural support of a building, the quoins at the corners as well as door and window surrounds, must be made of stone or brick. The nodules of flint may be used whole, but are most often split to produce a flat face, and sometimes knapped square. Village houses built on the Chalk downland use flint banded

Many of Ashmore's cottages include flint, Greensand and some brick.

or chequered with brick or stone as exterior facing. At Bere Regis church tower, built in about 1500, the flint is chequered with alternate blocks of Purbeck ashlar. In other places the flint is banded with different limestones according to the nearest source. In the Piddle valley, for instance, it is banded with lower Purbeck limestones. Surviving medieval buildings, such as the guest house at Cerne Abbey tend to use equal bands of flint and stone. In later years the proportion of flint seems to increase. Victorian masons knapped flint square more often than had been done earlier, producing a more ordered appearance to the building. Flint is black or dark brown, having a glassy texture, but exposure to the light over many centuries can result in fading of these dark colours. Each nodule has an outer porcellanous (chalky) crust originally white. However, where the flint has been redeposited as part of the Clay-with-Flints it may be stained pink by the minerals in the clay, and in the Plateau or Terrace Gravels it has been stained orange by iron oxides. An example of the pink staining can be seen in the cobbles at the Pitchmarket in Cerne Abbas, probably from the Clay-with-Flints near Giant's Head farm.

Although Flint is the most important building material on the Chalk downland across central Dorset, each river valley draining the downland has its own particular mixture of building materials, depending on its distance from the source of good stone. In the Frome valley Forest Marble, Chalk block, Cornbrash or Upper Greensand are used with flint in the upper reaches, but stone from the Ridgeway is used with flint nearer Dorchester.

[71]

DORSET HEATHS

Iron cemented sandstones known as heathstones have been quarried from three different deposits of Tertiary age (between 65 and 35 million years ago) for use in buildings. Because they were rare and of a rich brown colour which contrasted well with the pale cream of the Purbeck limestone or green of the Upper Greensand sandstone, they were highly prized and carried considerable distances for church building in the Winterborne and Tarrant valleys, and the Stour valley south-east of Blandford.

READING BEDS AND LONDON CLAY The Tertiary sands and clays were deposited on top of the Chalk as the sea level rose after millions of years in which Dorset had been part of a large continent; the sea advancing over an eroded Chalk landscape. The earliest deposits were pebble beds very similar to the rounded flint pebbles of the Chesil Beach today, followed by clays as the sea deepened. More pebble beds, sands and clays followed as the sea level fluctuated. The clays dug near Broadmayne were from the Reading Beds, and those in Corfe Mullen and north of Wimborne are London Clay. Knoll Manor Pit at Corfe Mullen has been used for brickmaking, and still provides clay for floor tiles. Within the London Clay the Lytchett Matravers Sand is an iron rich sandstone which when cut in large blocks for building can be seen to be current-bedded (lines of colour within the sandstone look like wave-ripples created by a current in the water). An even-textured, coarse-grained sandstone of a rich dark brown colour, it was quarried at Lytchett Matravers and also in patches on hills north of Wimborne. Its occurrence as rubble in farm buildings, a sure sign of a local source, seems to follow the outcrop of the Reading Beds and London Clay as far north as Cranborne.

As dressed stone, this rich brown sandstone has been carried some distance, notably to Tarrant Rushton where the medieval cruciform

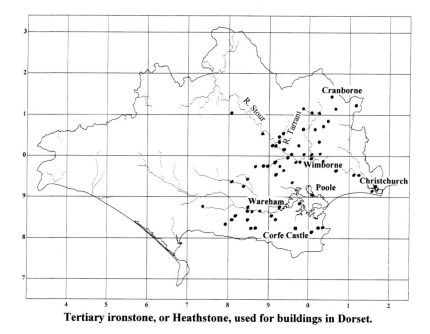

Tertiary ironstone, or Heathstone, used for buildings in Dorset.

church shows its rich colour beautifully. A window on the north side, with a view of the altar through a hagioscope (a hole in the wall for this purpose), is built of heathstone and clearly shows the marks of the fingers of lepers from a nearby hospital who took part in the service from outside. Lytchett Matravers and Corfe Mullen churches and the historic houses near to them have used this stone, while some still remains in the tower and plinth of Lytchett Minster church, rebuilt with Upton bricks in the nineteenth century. Julians Bridge in Wimborne was originally built (1636) of local sandstone, some of which is still visible underneath, but the later (1844) structure is of Purbeck-Portland limestone. The sandstone of the north wall and the tower of Wimborne Minster is in large blocks which appear to be the Lytchett Matravers Sandstone quarried in the area north towards Cranborne. At Kinson the twelfth century church tower is of similar large even-grained sandstone blocks. The sandstone has also been carried up the Stour to Sturminster Marshall, being used as rubble in the church, and dressed stone for the

White Mill Bridge on the River Stour is built of Lytchett Matravers Sandstone.

medieval bridge at White Mill. At Woodlands Farm near Verwood there is a retaining wall of large dressed blocks of heathstone.

POOLE FORMATION The Poole Formation above the London Clay has five cycles of sand and clay, with occasional lenses of sandstone which are variable in colour and texture. These were produced as a result of the weathering of a land area to the north and west. The shoreline is thought to have changed periodically, but south east Dorset was at that time part of a meandering river and estuary.

On the heathlands of the Poole Formation on either side of Poole Harbour, iron-cemented sandstones occur on top of the lenses of clay, or as isolated lenses of conglomerate within the sands. The colour of the sandstone ranges through deep blood red, scarlet, orange, and many shades of brown, and the texture may be fine to coarse sand, or a conglomerate (or mixture) of brown sandstone containing balls of orange clay. Several thick lenses of sandstone have recently been found during sand working at Henbury pit, Corfe Mullen, and this stone is currently being used for building or for repairing historic houses. At Studland the lowest part of the Poole Formation has been named the Redend Sandstone, with reference to Redend Point. A thick deposit was quarried at Woodhouse Hill and near Kingswood Farm, and several small diggings can be seen near Studland golf course. Each sandstone lens can vary in extent, colour, grain size and hardness. Some are thin and are used for paving around the heathland cottages. Some of the sandstones from the Poole Formation containing lumps of orange clay have been used as rubble or dressed stone in Wimborne Minster and Canford Magna church, where the stonework may be Saxon or Norman.

Sandstone from the Poole Formation is used on both sides of Poole Harbour, often mixed with Purbeck limestone – as in this barn at East Holme.

BARTON BEDS Above the Poole Formation the Branksome Sand completes the Bracklesham Group, which is followed by the Barton Group, made up of the Boscombe Sand, the Barton Clay, the Chama Bed and Becton Sands, mostly named after locations on the cliffs from Bournemouth eastwards. From Throop downstream on the Stour the heathstone used in building has a finer texture than that seen at Kinson or Wimborne, and the colour is blood-red to purple. This ironstone is not from the heath at all, but from Hengistbury Head, where there are two rows of doggers (hard rounded boulders) in the Barton Clay high on the cliff: as the cliff is undermined by the sea these fall to the beach. Before an attempt was made to exploit the ironstone in the nineteenth century, the beach was covered in these boulders and in the Middle Ages it was used as a rough building material for rubble walls, or the core of walls which were faced with better quality stone. A row of cottages at Holdenhurst has been built of stone from the medieval church, and in Christchurch the Priory ruins, the castle and the Constable's House all contain examples of ironstone, mixed with the limestones from Purbeck. In the Constable's House there is also a stone of the same colour but containing small white fossil gastropods which have been identified as from the Barton Beds in the cliffs further east.

CONCLUSION

The quarrying of local stone in the past has provided the visual character of the rural areas of Dorset. In the conurbation of the south east this character has been overwhelmed by twentieth century expansion, though even here a study of historic buildings can illustrate past connections with quarrying areas.

A study of the stone used in each village can record not only the geology, but also the history of family connections, of working practices, and of trade. In many villages the right of the inhabitants to draw stone from the parish quarry was recorded in Tudor times and the parish quarry was still identifiable at the time of the enclosures.

Transport for all this stone was by horse and cart over roads paved with chert, flint gravel, or limestone according to the nearest quarry, for each parish was responsible for maintaining its own roads. From the Waddon Hill account books, it would appear that roadstone was produced in greater quantities than building stone in the late nineteenth century, and this has probably always been the case. Only in Portland and Purbeck was quarrying a regular industry, with export from Dorset by sea. The advent of the railways in the Victorian age meant that other stone could be brought in, most noticeably Bath stone, which was used for door and window surrounds in churches in Poole and Bournemouth, the main walls being built of rock-faced Purbeck Freestone. The railways also brought roofing slate from Wales, to replace stone tiles or thatch. Stone tiles are heavy and need strong rafters, while thatch has been the cause of many disastrous fires, such as those in Beaminster and Blandford.

Since the beginning of the Second World War the majority of the small quarries in the countryside have closed, not for lack of stone but because the skilled craftsmanship required to build with stone is an expensive commodity. Little mechanisation can be achieved in quarrying the comparatively thin beds of limestone in most of the

The beauty of Dorset's building stones and the craftsmanship
of those who worked with them is well-illustrated in this
flint and limestone cottage in Puddletown.

Jurassic. In addition, except for the Purbeck and Portland limestones,
the reserves of stone are small and many of the deposits have been
worked out.

Many Dorset villages are now Conservation Areas with thousands
of buildings listed as of historic or architectural interest by English
Heritage. Repair and maintenance require the use of the original
stone. Maintaining the character of Conservation Areas when adding
new buildings also requires the use of the original stone, or at least
one from the same formation which can match it in colour and
texture. It is a mistake to think that 'stone is stone'. One only has to
look at the grey Purbeck stone houses in Trent, contrasted with the
cream Inferior Oolite almshouses and school to see that the visual
character has been changed. In some villages reconstituted stone has
been coloured to match the local one, but its regular blocks and
bland texture give the game away. It is my belief that the rich
character of our Dorset villages can only be maintained if small
quarries can continue in use for repairs, additions and new building.
They are our heritage, and a study of the individual types of stone
can illustrate the unwritten history of the county of Dorset. The
examples given in this book are simply a few of the thousands of
listed buildings which have been constructed of local materials.

FURTHER READING

Arkell, W. J., The names of the strata in the Purbeck & Portland stone quarries. *Dorset Proceedings, 66*, 158-68, 1945

Oxford Stone. Faber & Faber, 1947

Arkell, W. J. & Tomkeieff, S.I., *English Rock Terms. Chiefly used by miners and quarrymen*. Oxford, 1953

Beaumont-Slegge, W., Mason's marks in Dorset churches. *Dorset Proceedings,* 71, 73, 1950

Benfield, Eric, *Purbeck Shop. A Stoneworker's Story of Stone*. Introduction by Brian Bugler. Ensign, 1990

Brocklebank, J., *Victorian stone carvers in Dorset churches*. 1856-1880. Dovecote Press, 1979

Clements, R.G., Type-section of the Purbeck Limestone Group, Durlston Bay, Swanage, Dorset. *Dorset Proceedings,* 114, 181-206, 1993

Cockburn, E.O. *The development of stone quarrying in Dorset*. Ms in Dorset County Museum, 1971

Fowler, J., *The stones of Sherborne Abbey*. Sherborne, 1938

Hutchins, J., *History and antiquities of the county of Dorset*. 3rd edn. (1st edn. 1774, 2nd edn. 1796-1815), 1861-1870

Jones, I., *The Stalbridge Inheritance*. Larkwood, 1993

Leach, R., *An investigation into the use of Purbeck Marble in medieval England,* Harrison, 1975

Newman, J. & Pevsner, N., *The buildings of England. Dorset*. Penguin, 1972, 2nd edn. 1985

Royal Commission on Historical Monuments, vol. 1: West Dorset (1952), vol. 2: South East Dorset (1970), vol. 3: Central Dorset (1970), vol. 4: North Dorset (1972), vol. 5: East Dorset (1975)

Thomas, J., The Building Stones of Dorset: Part 1. The Western parishes. Upper Greensand Chert and Lower Lias. *Dorset Proceedings* 114, 1993

Part 2. Chideock to Broadwinsor – Middle and Upper Lias. *Dorset Proceedings* 115, 1994

Part 3. Inferior Oolite, Forest Marble, Cornbrash and Corallian Limestone. *Dorset Proceedings* 116, 1995

Part 4. The northern parishes which use Forest Marble and Cornbrash limestones. *Dorset Proceedings* 117, 1996

ACKNOWLEDGEMENTS

My thanks are due to the working quarrymen, particularly Trev Haysom and Lloyd Warren, who helped me with so much information; to the many farmers who allowed me to visit the old quarries on their land; to the staff of the Dorset County Record Office; to John Lowe, the Historic Buildings Officer of Dorset County Council, and the owners of innumerable historic buildings; to Paul Ensom and many geological colleagues; and last but not least my infinitely patient and long-suffering husband.

Most of the photographs in this book were taken by the author, but Jo Thomas would like to thank the following for allowing the inclusion of illustrations in their possession or for which they hold the copyright. British Geological Survey: pages 13, 14 (top); The Bridport Museum Service: page 25; Christopher Chaplin: the general geological map on page 9 (with thanks also to Dr M. E. Cosgrove and the Dorset Wildlife Trust); Dorset County Museum: front cover; The Dovecote Press Collection: frontispiece, copyright page, pages 32, 40, 42, 51 (top), 53, 57, 66, 71, 74, 77; Stuart Morris: pages 15 (top), 52; Mr. Lloyd Warren: page 14 (bottom).

The

DISCOVER DORSET

Series of Books

A series of paperback books providing informative illustrated
introductions to Dorset's history, culture and way of life.
The following titles have so far been published.

BLACKMORE VALE *Hilary Townsend*
BRIDGES *David McFetrich and Jo Parsons*
CASTLES & FORTS *Colin Pomeroy*   COAST & SEA *Sarah Welton*
CRANBORNE CHASE *Desmond Hawkins*
DOWNS, MEADOWS & PASTURES *Jim White*
DRESS & TEXTILES *Rachel Worth*
FARMHOUSES & COTTAGES *Michael Billett*
FARMING *J.H.Bettey*   FOLLIES *Jonathan Holt*
FOSSILS *Richard Edmonds*   GEOLOGY *Paul Ensom*
THE GEORGIANS *Jo Draper*   HEATHLANDS *Lesley Haskins*
THE INDUSTRIAL PAST *Peter Stanier*
ISLE OF PURBECK *Paul Hyland*   LEGENDS *Jeremy Harte*
LOST VILLAGES *Linda Viner*   MILLS *Peter Stanier*
PORTLAND *Stuart Morris*   POTTERY *Penny Copland-Griffiths*
THE PREHISTORIC AGE *Bill Putnam*
RAILWAY STATIONS *Mike Oakley*
REGENCY, RIOT & REFORM *Jo Draper*
RIVERS & STREAMS *John Wright*   THE ROMANS *Bill Putnam*
SAXONS & VIKINGS *David Hinton*   SHIPWRECKS *Maureen Attwooll*
STONE QUARRYING *Jo Thomas*   TUDORS & STUARTS *J.H. Bettey*
THE VICTORIANS *Jude James*   WOODLANDS *Anne Horsfall*

All the books about Dorset published by The Dovecote Press
are available in bookshops throughout the county,
or in case of difficulty direct from the publishers.
The Dovecote Press Ltd, Stanbridge,
Wimborne Minster, Dorset BH21 4JD
Tel: 01258 840549   www.dovecotepress.com